79p

Postman Pat
Annual 1986

Dear Girls and Boys,
Here is a book especially
for you. Everyone from
Greendale is here and
you can share with us all
the seasons of the year.
There are stories and
puzzles—I even tell
a few jokes !
Cheerio for now.
Love from,
Postman Pat
and Jess.

× × ×

The Greendale Folk

Pat, Sara, Julian & Jess

Granny Dryden

Sam Waldron

Rebecca Hubbard

Alf Thompson

Dorothy & Bill Thompson

Reverend Timms

George Lancaster

Ted Glen

Colonel Forbes

Mrs Goggins

Doctor Gilbertson

Mrs Pottage & Paul

Tom & Katy Pottage

Peter Fogg

The field-mouse

1 Pat was helping the Reverend Timms decorate the church for the Harvest Festival. "Doesn't it look nice?" said Pat, setting out the fruit.

2 "Mrs Pottage's carrots are huge," said the Reverend Timms, laying them out on display. "They look very tasty indeed."

3 Alf Thompson arrived with some sheaves of barley. "I thought these would look nice in the church, Reverend," he said.

4 Pat arranged them on the display. He had to move Mrs Pottage's carrots to make room. "What a size!" he said.

5 Jess peeked out from one of the pews to watch. Pat and the Reverend went to fetch vases for the bunches of flowers.

6 When they came back, Jess was staring at the display. "Come away," said Pat. "Don't touch anything." Jess miaowed.

7 Pat went to see what Jess was looking at. "Well I never," he whispered. "A mouse is eating one of the carrots!"

8 Sure enough, a little field-mouse was nibbling a carrot. "It must have been hiding in those sheaves," said Pat.

9 The mouse was so busy eating, it did not notice Pat creeping up on it. "Got it!" said Pat, placing his cap on it.

10 Carefully, Pat carried the mouse out of the church. "This is where you belong," he said, letting it go in the long grass.

11 "Thank goodness Jess spotted it," said the Reverend Timms. "Otherwise it may have eaten all Mrs Pottage's carrots!"

Can you help the field-mouse find his way
through the long grass to his friends?

Jess the cat mask

Trace this picture of Jess on to paper. Colour it in and cut it out. Cut holes for your eyes and nose. Make small holes in each side and thread string through them. Tie it at the back of your head.

How many things can you see in the picture starting with the letter b?

Peter Fogg's jigsaw

Trace the picture on to paper and colour it in.
Then stick it on to card and cut out the pieces.

The unusual pet

1 "Are you entering Jess for the Pet Show?" Colonel Forbes asked Pat. "There's a cat section and an unusual pet competition."

2 "I'll enter him in the cat section," said Pat. He drove off. "I wonder what unusual pets there will be?" he said.

3 The day of the Pet Show came. "I hope the rain goes off," said Pat, looking out the window. "It will be so muddy."

4 At last the rain stopped and the sun shone. "Come on, Jess," said Pat. "We're off to the show." But Jess had gone.

5 Pat hunted in the garden. "Jess? Where are you?" he called. He found him hiding under the hedge. "Come out," said Pat.

6 Pat had a shock when he saw Jess. "You look like a hedgehog!" he gasped. Jess had been rolling in the mud and twigs.

7 "You won't win a prize looking like that!" As they drove to the Pet Show, Pat had an idea. "I wonder?" he said.

8 Pat decided to enter Jess in the unusual pet competition. "You certainly don't look your usual self, Jess," he chuckled.

9 "And first prize for an unusual pet goes to Jess, the hedgecat, or, er, pussyhog," said Colonel Forbes. Pat just smiled to himself.

Jess is playing with his friends.
But which cat is Jess? Look closely.

Leaf print writing paper

Lay a leaf in a saucer of paint.
Print the leaf, paint-side down
on to a sheet of paper. Use leaves
of different shapes. You could
print them on to envelopes, too.

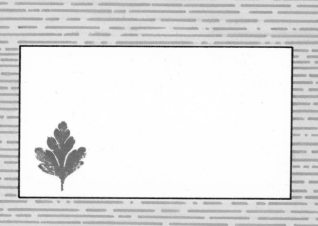

The misty morning

1 Mist was covering the valley when Pat set off on his round, one morning. "I can hardly see where I'm going," he told Jess. "I hope it lifts soon."

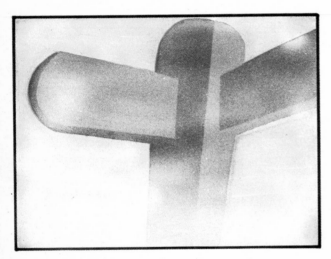

2 Pat drove slowly. "Everything looks so different," he said, peering through the mist. "There's someone wanting a lift."

3 But when Pat stopped by the man, he saw it was only a signpost. "Silly me," he chuckled. "This mist plays tricks."

4 Pat was still chuckling as he drove on. Suddenly, he let out a yell. "A ghost!" he cried, pointing to a white shape.

5 The shape came closer. "Baa!" it said. "It's only one of Alf Thompson's sheep!" said Pat. "What a fright it gave me."

6 "I hope I don't have any more tricks played on me by this mist," said Pat. "I've had quite enough for one day."

7 Then, Pat saw another figure by the roadside. "Look!" he said. "There's another signpost. It won't trick me."

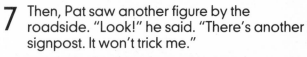

8 "Hey!" someone shouted, as Pat drove on. "Stop!" Peter Fogg came running up. "Didn't you see me there, Pat?"

9 "I thought you were a signpost," Pat explained. "It's the mist. It makes it difficult to make things out properly."

10 Pat drove Peter Fogg to Greendale Farm. "Thanks, Pat," he said. "Hope you don't meet any more strange signposts today."

11 As Pat drove on down the valley, the mist began to lift and things looked more normal. "That's better," said Pat.

Help Pat find his way back to Greendale through the mist.

Pat and his friends are sledging. Follow the trails in the snow to find out where each one started.

The Power failure

1 "What on earth's that?" Pat asked Ted Glen when he called with a letter. "It's a wood burning stove," said Ted. "It will come in useful one day."

2 "Wood burning stove," Pat said to Jess as he drove off. "What will Ted collect next?" It was cold when Pat arrived home.

3 "Brr," he said. "It's a night for a hot meal and a seat in front of the television. Oh good, sausages for tea."

4 "Help me cook them," said Sara. Then, the lights went out. "A power failure!" said Pat. "Hope it doesn't last long."

5 "We can't cook the sausages," said Sara. "There's no electricity." "We can't watch television, either," moaned Pat.

6 There was a knock at the door. It was Ted. "I'm setting up my wood burning stove in the church hall," he said.

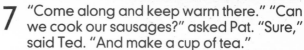

7 "Come along and keep warm there." "Can we cook our sausages?" asked Pat. "Sure," said Ted. "And make a cup of tea."

8 Soon everyone in Greendale was crowding into the hall. Ted had lit the stove and it was warm. He put seats round it.

9 The Reverend Timms brought candles from the church. Mrs Goggins put the kettle on the stove and Pat cooked sausages.

10 Miss Hubbard made sandwiches. "They're crabmeat," she said. "I'll stick to sausages," said Pat.

11 After tea, they sat by the stove telling stories. "This is fun," said Pat. "Told you my stove would be useful," said Ted.

Everything looks different by candle-light.
Can you work out who is sitting here?

Pat's special sausages

Cook some sausages and stick them into a big mound of mashed potato so that it looks like a hedgehog! The hedgehog's nose is a pea!

The talent show

1 "Are you taking part in the talent show?" Mrs Goggins asked Pat. "I don't know what to do," said Pat. "You could tell jokes," said Mrs Goggins.

2 Pat asked everybody on his round if they knew any jokes. The Pottage twins knew lots. Pat laughed at all of them.

3 At the talent show, the twins played a piano duet and everyone clapped. "You play well," said Pat. "That was good."

4 Then it was Ted Glen's turn. He played tunes using two spoons. The audience really enjoyed it and gave him a cheer.

5 Miss Hubbard sang loudly. Everyone joined in the chorus. She sang until she was hoarse and she had to stop.

6 "Who's next?" asked the Reverend Timms. "Would someone like to come on stage and entertain us with some jokes?"

7 "Pat can tell jokes," shouted Tom. "Go on," said Katy. "I hope I can remember them," said Pat, climbing up the steps.

8 Pat looked down at all the people. "Um," he said. "Good man," said Ted. "That's the stuff. Come on, let's hear them."

9 "Have you heard the one about the two eggs?" said Pat. "No!" they all shouted. "Two bad!" said Pat. Everyone laughed.

10 "Tell us another one, Pat," called Ted. "That was good." Pat told all the jokes he knew and the audience applauded him.

11 The talent show was a great success. "Thank you to all who took part," said the Reverend. "We enjoyed it immensely."

Pat loves telling jokes. Here are some of his favourites.

Who gets the sack as soon as he starts work? A postman!

What does Mrs Pottage rub on the pig when it is sick? Oinkment!

Why does Miss Hubbard rest her bike against a wall? Because it is two tyred!

Shall I tell you the joke about the butter? I'd better not, you'll only spread it!

Sing the Postman Pat song with Pat

Postman Pat
Postman Pat
Postman Pat and his black and white cat
Early in the morning
Just as day is dawning
Picks up all the post-bags in his van

Postman Pat
Postman Pat
Postman Pat and his black and white cat
All the birds are singing
And the day is just beginning
Pat feels he's a really happy man

Everybody knows his bright red van
All his friends will smile
As he waves to greet them
Maybe, you can never be sure
There'll be . . .
Knock! Ring!
Letters through your door

Postman Pat
Postman Pat
Postman Pat and his black
and white cat
All the birds are singing
And the day is just beginning
Pat feels he's a really happy man
Pat feels he's a really happy man.

A snowy day

1 It had been snowing hard. "I'll have to dig a path to the gate," said Pat, looking out of the window. "It's too deep to walk in."

2 Pat worked hard, digging away the snow until he could see the path underneath. At last, he reached the front gate.

3 "I'd better take the spade with me in case I have to do some more digging," he said, putting it in the van. "Come on, Jess."

4 Pat drove carefully. The trees and hedges were covered in snow. "Look, Jess," said Pat. "The snow is right over that fence."

5 Then he had to stop. Sam Waldron's mobile shop was stuck in the snow in front. "Have you got a spade, Pat?" Sam asked.

6 Pat took out his spade and dug the snow from under the wheels. Sam started the engine. "Thanks, Pat," he said.

7 "Just as well I brought the spade," Pat said to Jess, as he climbed into the van. He drove along to Thompson Ground.

8 Alf looked worried. "What's wrong?" Pat asked. "My sheep are buried in the snow," he said. "I have to dig them out."

9 "I have a spade," said Pat. He started to dig away the snow. "Here they are," he called. "Baa," said a cold sheep.

10 The sheep were pleased to get out of the snow. "They'll be hungry. I'll put out some hay," said Alf. "Thanks, Pat."

11 ."A spade's a very useful thing in the snow," Pat said to Jess. But Jess was not listening. He was fast asleep.

Through the seasons

spring

summer

with Postman Pat

autumn

winter

Granny Dryden's tea-cosy

Granny Dryden was spring-cleaning.

"Will you take all this old stuff down to the church hall for me, Pat?" she asked. "They're having a jumble sale on Saturday."

"Why are you throwing out your tea-cosy?" said Pat, holding it up. "What's wrong with it?"

"I have a new one now," she said. "So I don't need my old one any more."

Pat loaded the jumble into his van and drove off. Granny Dryden put the kettle on to make a cup of tea. She got out her new tea-cosy.

"Doesn't it look smart?" she said. "Much nicer than my old one." But when she tried to put it over her teapot, it was too big.

"Oh, dear," she said. "It's not such a good fit as the old one was." And when she poured the tea, it dribbled down the tea-cosy and soaked it.

"Bother," she said. "My old one never did that." So she took the tea-cosy off. But when she poured herself another cup of tea, she found that the tea was cold.

"My, oh my," she said. "I wish I'd never given my old tea-cosy to the jumble sale. It was much better than this one."

"I'll buy that tea-cosy," she said to Miss Hubbard, who was in charge.

"Certainly," replied Miss Hubbard, handing it to her.

Pat gave Granny Dryden a lift back to her cottage in his van.

"What did you buy at the jumble sale?" he asked.

"I bought my old tea-cosy," she told him. "It fits my teapot, it doesn't get wet and it keeps my tea warm. You never know how useful things are until you throw them out." Pat and Granny Dryden drove home laughing.

Granny Dryden waited impatiently for Saturday and the jumble sale. When it opened, she marched up to the stall where her old tea-cosy was lying.

A wedding invitation

1 "There's a letter for you this morning, Pat," said Mrs Goggins. "I wonder who it's from?" said Pat, opening it eagerly.

Pat and Sara
PLEASE COME
TO MY
WEDDING
Jim

2 It was a wedding invitation. "Jim the Pencaster postman is getting married and Sara and I are invited," said Pat.

3 When Pat finished his round, he and Sara went shopping. "I'd like a suit," said Pat. "I want a hat," said Sara.

4 Pat tried on several suits. "I like this one," he said. "It looks good," said Sara, who was at the hat counter.

5 "What do you think of this hat?" Sara asked Pat. "Is it a bit too fancy?" "No," replied Pat. "It really suits you."

6 Then they went to buy Jim's present. "What would he like?" asked Sara. "He always likes a cup of tea," said Pat.

7 They bought a teapot with roses on it. "It'll make him plenty of cups of tea," said Pat. They drove to Jim's house.

8 Jim was pleased to see them. "Come in," he said. Pat gave him the present. "How kind," said Jim. "Thanks very much."

9 Jim opened the parcel and took out the teapot. "Lovely," he said. "Just what I need. You know I like a cup of tea."

10 "I'll try it out now." Jim put on the kettle and, while they were waiting, he showed Pat and Sara the wedding presents.

11 Then they had a cup of tea from the new teapot. "Makes a nice cup of tea," said Pat. "Yes," said Jim. "Thank you both."

Granny Dryden has knitted a present for Jim, the Pencaster postman. Join the dots to find out what it is.

Mrs Pottage's chocolate treats

Ask someone to make these for you.

Melt 3oz of chocolate in a bowl over a pan of hot water. Add the yoke of an egg, ½oz of butter and 1tsp of cream. Beat the mixture until it is thick. Chill it in the fridge. Shape into balls and toss in chocolate hail or dessicated coconut. Eat them!

Jim's wedding

1 It was the day of Jim's wedding. Pat was up bright and early so he would finish his round in time to get to the church to see Jim married.

2 The sun was shining and the birds were singing. Pat sang, too, as he drove. "Lovely day for a wedding," he said.

3 The twins were putting on new outfits for the wedding. "You look very smart," Pat said. "See you later in church."

4 "Do you like my new hat?" Miss Hubbard asked Pat, when he called. "It's very striking," said Pat, avoiding a feather.

5 Ted Glen was hunting for his tie. "Don't know when I last wore it," he said. "It must be here somewhere. Ah, found it!"

6 When Pat finished his round, he dashed home to change. "Hurry up," said Sara. "It's nearly time for us to leave."

7 "Don't we look a pair of swells?" said Pat, looking in the mirror. Sara pinned a pink flower in his buttonhole.

8 The church was crowded when they arrived. Reverend Timms was dressed in his robes, Jim stood beside him looking shy.

9 When Meg the bride arrived, the organ played. The Reverend Timms married them and Jim and Meg walked down the aisle.

10 Outside the church the photographer was busy. "Smile please," he called. Pat stood behind Jim for the wedding photographs.

11 It took a long while to take everyone's photos. At last it was over. "Right," said Jim. "Time for a nice cup of tea."

Pat's Birthday Surprise

"Has Pat gone on his round?" Dorothy Thompson asked Mrs Goggins, one morning.

"Yes, he left ten minutes ago," said Mrs Goggins. "Why?"

"Listen," said Mrs Thompson. She whispered something in Mrs Goggins ear. Mrs Goggins smiled. "That will be nice," she said.

Meanwhile, Pat was on his way to Thompson Ground. He was looking rather sad.

"No letters for me today, Jess," he said. "But I've got one for Alf Thompson." Alf was waiting for him.

"Come in and have a cup of tea," he said.

Pat sat down at the table. When he finished his tea, he stood up and said, "That was good. Thanks, Alf. I'd better be off now."

"Oh, er, no hurry, Pat. Have some more tea," replied Alf, filling his cup. Pat sat down and drank it.

"I really must be off now, Alf. I'll see you tomorrow."

"I'm driving my tractor down to the valley," said Alf. "I'll go first."

Pat followed Alf in his tractor.

"Why is he going so slowly? I'm never going to finish my round at this rate," said Pat, grumpily.

It took a long time for Pat to deliver all his letters because Alf was chugging slowly along the road in front of him.

"Where on earth is he going?" said Pat, as Alf drove along the main street and stopped outside Pat's house.

"Here we are," said Alf. "Did I slow him down enough?"

"Yes," said Dorothy Thompson, coming out of Pat's house. "Everything's ready."

Somewhat bewildered, Pat followed Dorothy into the house. As she opened the door, everyone shouted, "HAPPY BIRTHDAY, PAT!"

"Well, I never," said Pat, looking around in surprise. "I thought nobody had remembered it was my birthday."

"We were keeping it quiet," said Sara. "So it would be a surprise for you."

"It certainly was," said Pat, beaming happily.

Here is another surprise for Pat. Presents!
There is a book, a pot plant, a fishing-rod
and a pair of wellington boots. Can you
guess which is which?

Pat's birthday pudding

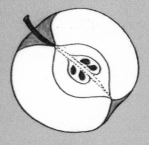  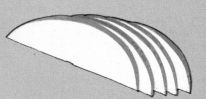

Slice an apple thinly and put it in a bowl with some grapes.
Pour natural yoghurt on top and mix it all together.

Pat has added chocolate sweets
as a special treat, but usually
he likes to eat it plain.

Miss Hubbard's apple wine

It was a crisp autumn morning. Pat stopped outside Miss Hubbard's house with some letters to deliver.

"Come on, Jess," he said, as he walked up the path. "You can come, too."

"Hello, Pat," said Miss Hubbard, as she opened the door. "Come in, I could do with your help."

Pat followed her into the kitchen. There was a strange noise coming from it.

Plop, pop, gurgle, gurgle. Plop, pop, gurgle, gurgle.

"Whatever's that?" Pat asked. He stared at a collection of glass jars and pipes all bubbling and gurgling noisily.

"It's my apple wine," said Miss Hubbard. "I'm going to bottle it." Pat held the bottles while Miss Hubbard filled them with her apple wine.

"It smells a bit funny," said Pat. "Is it supposed to?"

"This is special wine," said Miss Hubbard. "It might win a prize at the Greendale Show."

When all the bottles were filled, Miss Hubbard put corks in them.

"Don't they look good?" she said, proudly. "And such a lovely colour." She held one up to the light to show Pat. POP! Suddenly, a cork shot off and whizzed past Pat's ear. POP! The cork from another bottle shot into the air.

"Duck, Jess!" yelled Pat, as corks shot everywhere.

POP! POP! POP!

"Oh, goodness me!" said Miss Hubbard, from behind a chair. "I think the wine must have been a little too strong."

"It must be powerful stuff," said Pat, from under the table.

At last, the corks stopped popping and Pat crawled out from his hiding place.

"I wonder what went wrong?" said Miss Hubbard. "I hope the rest of my wine is all right. Would you like to see it, Pat?"

"Er, no thanks," said Pat, reaching for his cap. "We'd better be off now."

Pat and Jess jumped into the van and drove off.

"Phew!" said Pat. "I think I'll stick to making tea. It's safer!"

Spot the difference

At first glance, these pictures may look the same. Look carefully and see how many differences you can spot.

Katy and Tom's apple games

Tie an apple to a string or float apples in a bowl of water. Try to take a bite, without using your hands!

Make apple teeth by cutting teeth shapes from apple.

Pat's seaside crossword

Across:
1 Lives in the sea
5 Pat paddles in it
6 Your favourite postman
8 Can nip your toe

Down:
2 Pat likes to eat it
3 Can help you find treasure
4 The sun makes you feel this
7 Julian is eating one

Can you read the letter Julian has written?

Dear 🐿 and 🐑

👁 am at the 🌊 with 👴 and 👩. It is ☀.

We built a ⛱ and went 4 a 🏊. Then 🐺 🪚 a 🦀. 👁 8 a big 🍦. Yum!

See U soon,

love from 👵 XX

Alf plays a trick

1 "Come and see the marrow I've grown," Dorothy Thompson said to Pat. "I'm entering it in the Greendale Show. Do you think it will win?"

2 "What a huge marrow!" said Pat, amazed. "I've never seen one that big before. I'm sure it will take first prize."

3 "Rubbish," said Alf, passing by on his tractor. "Wait till you see the ones in the show. They'll be bigger than that."

4 "Stop teasing," said Dorothy, laughing. "You're as proud of it as I am." "I've never grown one as big as that," Pat said.

5 On the morning of the show, Dorothy carefully carried her marrow to the judging tent. "Hope it wins," she said.

6 But when she arrived, she had a surprise. An even bigger marrow was entered in the competition. "Who grew that?" she said.

7 She bent to look at the label. BANG! The marrow burst. "My goodness," she said. "It must have been a balloon."

8 Behind her, Alf was chuckling. "Oh, you," said Dorothy, smiling. "Up to tricks again. You put that balloon there."

9 When the judge pinned first prize on her marrow, everyone cheered. "Well done, Dorothy. I knew you'd win," said Alf.

Alf Thompson likes playing games. He has written the word 'joke' ten times in this box of letters. Can you find them?

N	A	D	J	O	K	E	O
S	B	J	O	N	T	D	E
V	J	O	K	E	N	J	Q
J	O	K	E	C	S	O	R
A	K	E	F	J	O	K	E
M	E	L	T	O	P	E	R
Z	Y	J	O	K	E	N	T
F	C	B	D	E	B	P	I

Bookmarks

Trace your favourite character on to thin card.
Colour it in and cut carefully around the dotted lines.

Visitors to Greendale

1 Pat was driving through Greendale when he saw a car parked at the side of the road. "Hello, what's up?" he said. "Someone in trouble?"

2 "Anything wrong?" he asked, stopping beside the car. "We're lost," said a man in a flowery shirt. "Can you help?"

3 Pat got out of the van to look at the map the man was holding. "We want to go there," said the man. "We're tourists."

4 "You're on the wrong road," Pat said. "Follow me and I'll show you the way." Pat drove off and the tourists followed.

5 Pat had to call at Thompson Ground with a letter. "Won't be a moment," he said to the tourists. "Wait here for me."

6 While Pat was giving the letter to Alf, the tourists began taking photographs. Click, click, went their cameras.

7 "Why are they taking photos of us?" Alf asked. "They're from America," said Pat. "They don't have farms like this."

8 "Just love your country," said the man, taking a photo of Pat and Jess. "Smile please." Pat straightened his tie.

9 Pat took the tourists to the road they wanted. "Keep going for five miles," he said. "Gee, thanks," they said, waving.

10 "Fancy coming all the way from America to visit Greendale," Pat said to Jess. "I hope the photos turn out all right."

11 A few weeks later, Pat received a letter with American stamps on it. Inside was a photo. "Isn't that nice?" said Pat.

Pat's jumbled photographs game

Can you find the correct body for each head?

Pat and Ted's fishing-lines have become tangled.
Can you untangle them to see what they have caught?

Pat's Picnic

1 It was a warm summer's day, so Pat decided to have his lunch in a field. "We'll have a picnic, Jess," he said. "Would you like that?"

2 Jess purred loudly. Pat stopped the van and he and Jess climbed a fence into a field. "This will do nicely," said Pat.

3 Suddenly, Pat saw something move. "Oh, dear," he said. "It's Hector the bull. I don't think he likes us being here."

4 Pat and Jess scrambled through the fence. "Let's try somewhere else," said Pat, as he drove off along the road.

5 Pat found a nice shady spot under a tree. "No bulls here," he said, looking about. He sat down and took out his sandwiches.

6 "Cluck, cluck," called some hens as they came running up. "Shoo!" cried Pat. "Go away! Don't eat my lunch, I'm hungry."

7 The hens liked sandwiches. Pat threw some crumbs. "Come on, Jess," he said. "Let's go before they eat everything."

8 "Let's try the river," said Pat. Soon they were sitting on the bank. "This is better," he said, munching his lunch.

9 "Buzz! Buzz!" A swarm of flies landed on the sandwiches. "Get off!" shouted Pat. "Scram!" But the flies stayed.

10 So Pat and Jess went back to the van. "Never mind, Jess. I know a spot with no bulls, no hens and no flies."

11 "Why didn't I come here first?" Pat said, as he settled comfortably on his garden seat. "My own garden is perfect!"

Postman Pat's river race

Pat is rowing on the river. Can you help him home in time for dinner?

You need a dice and a different coloured counter for each player. Throw the dice to see how many squares to move. The winner is the first one to reach the finish.

START

1

2

JESS OVERBOARD. MISS A TURN.

3

4

STRONG CURRENT. ON 4 SPACES.

20

19

21

22

23

24

CAUGHT IN THICK REEDS. MISS A TURN.

25

26

27

28

GETTING HUNGRY. SPEED UP 3 PLACES.

29

30

31

45

44

43

42

46

47 STOP TO PLAY HIDE-AND-SEEK. MISS A TURN.

48

CATCH A FISH. ON 3 SPACES.

49

50

51

52

53

THE POSTMAN PAT ANNUAL is published by Polystyle Publications Limited, London, NW1.
Typesetting by Paul Hicks Limited, Plymouth, Devon. Printed in Italy
for Saltway Limited. Trade distribution by Argus Press Sales and Distribution
Limited, 12–18 Paul Street, London, EC2A 4JS. Tel: 01-247 8233.   ISBN 85096 121 1